ALEWIFE'S GARDEN

7 Radical Weeds for Brewing Herbal Ales

Cultivate High Spirits

**Basil · Borage · Caraway · Coriander
Hyssop · Winter Savory · Yarrow**

A GARDEN REMEDY BOOK WITH FREE SEEDS BY

Jillian VanNostrand & Christie V. Sarles

ILLUSTRATIONS BY

Marty Copplestone

A toast to all who spread
Radical Weeds
&
Special thanks to Stephen Buhner
who introduced us to
the deep magic of yeast

Simple Books with Free, Fresh Seeds
There's a garden in every one . . .
Everyone into the garden!

Published by Radical Weeds
P.O. Box 68, Mirror Lake, NH 03853-0068
Copyright ©2002 by Jillian VanNostrand and Christie V. Sarles
All rights reserved.

ISBN 0-9664246-3-8

Book design by Praying Mantis Graphics
Printed in Canada

Only you have the power to take responsibility for all of your health care decisions. Consult your own inner wisdom, and check with your health practitioner and herbalist for guidance in making informed choices about your own unique body in relation to any of the contents of this book.
No guarantees.

TABLE OF CONTENTS

1
Step Into Our Garden

2
Alewife's Garden

5
Basil

7
Borage

9
Caraway

11
Coriander

13
Hyssop

15
Winter Savory

17
Yarrow

18
Starting Seeds Indoors & Out

21
Harvesting & Storing Plants & Seeds

22
Brewing Simple Ales
Ingredients — Equipment — Process

25
Additional Resources
Books & Supplies

27
Postcard for Free Seeds
Postcard for Radical Weeds Mailing List

Step into our garden...

We two sisters have worked with radical weeds for more than 30 years. "Radical" comes from the Latin *radix* — literally, "root." By "weed," we mean any plant that you can cultivate and use as a source of your strength and vitality. We've grown and used radical weeds for ourselves, our families and friends, a midwifery practice, two herbal mail order businesses, and countless workshops and weedwalks.

Alewife's Garden has been brewing since 1997. Since then, we've fed a lot of fermented wort to the chickens and the compost pile (it's great for both). More often, though, we've toasted our efforts with some truly memorable ales, including every recipe you'll find in this book.

Our goal for Alewife's Garden is to simplify and streamline home brewing with herbs. We invite you to share the delicious, nutritious, health-giving ales field-tested in our own kitchens. Making ale doesn't get any simpler than this. Send for your seeds, and remember to pass some along.

Here's to spreading the bounty of radical weeds and the magic of fermentation into many lives and places!

Jillian & Christie

Alewife's Garden

To your health! This ancient toast to wellbeing has its roots in a time when home-brewed herbal ales truly had the power to nourish and heal as well as to inebriate. The stories and traditions of every culture on Earth tell of fermentation as a gift from the Mother, given to her children to ease both spiritual and physical knowledge of our mortality.

Yeast is the agent of transformation that alewives once named Spirit. For millennia, women served as sole guardians of the divine gift of Spirit, and brewing for the household was serious — sacred — women's work. The ceremonies and beliefs surrounding the entire process of fermenting herbs into heady and healing elixirs connected the whole community to Source.

In the beginning, the alewife used herbs, honeys, and yeasts to brew simple ales. Her fermenters were gourds and pots left open to attract wild yeasts, and she evolved all kinds of rituals to draw Spirit into the brew for the goodness of the ale. Many plants, strains of yeast, and fermentable sugars were used. Each successful combination of these basic ingredients yielded a yeasty "starter" for the next brewing and a uniquely flavored drink — the signature of a household's hospitality and a cornerstone of community health.

Brewing herbs enhances their nutritional value. The protein and B vitamin content of herbal ales is significantly increased over levels found in the herbs themselves. Through fermentation, herbal ales become higher-powered energy foods and tonics. The ales you make from any of the herbs in Alewife's Garden will be about 3% alcohol, and the nutritive value of the plants will be quickly assimilated by your body, using alcohol as the carrier. The alcohol in these ales also carries high spirits to heal your soul.

The seven radical weeds in Alewife's Garden are cultivated for their tonic digestive effects, nutritive and medicinal values, and consciousness expanding properties. Traditional bitter brewing herbs like Caraway, Coriander, Hyssop, and Yarrow stimulate digestion and support liver function. Besides adding flavor and aroma to ales, pungent Basil and peppery Winter Savory are also excellent digestives. Borage makes a sweet, light-tasting ale, with all of the antidepressant and tonic qualities of the plant. In addition to its medicinal benefits, Yarrow can be brewed specifically for its highly inebriating, psychotropic, and aphrodisiac effects. Basil, Coriander, and Winter Savory have also been used to stimulate passion.

Our relationship to fermented beverages becomes essentially healthful and natural when we are the creators of a brewing process that provides nourishment for body and soul. When you invite Spirit back into home brewing, you honor your own kitchen as sacred space, and acknowledge your deep-rooted connection to Source.

In Alewife's Garden, you tend a legendary gift as old as humanity, and of infinite possibility. Give thanks for the magic of fermentation as you stir yeast into the brew. Reconnect with Spirit. Brew your health!

Basil *Ocimum basilicum, Common Basil*

Basil is a holy herb in its native India, an incarnation of Lakshmi, Goddess of abundance. It grows in pots at the doorways of Hindu temples and homes, and people customarily eat a few leaves daily for digestion. Basil's digestive and sedative actions calm stomach cramps and relieve gas pains and nausea, especially nausea from chemotherapy. Before pesto, Westerners also used Basil as a love charm, and it does have properties that stimulate and enhance production of sexual hormones.

USES

○ Provides tonic nourishment
○ Aids digestion
○ Relieves cramps, gas, nausea
○ Excites passion

CULTIVATION

Basil grows easily from seed. Use pots to start inside, as it develops quite a tap root. To direct seed outside, wait until after the last frost. (More about starting seeds on page 18.) Basil loves rich, composted soil and a warm, sunny, protected spot. Grows up to 2 feet high, with bright green, aromatic leaves 2-3 inches long and small white flowers on stalks at the tops of the stems. Harvest the leafy tops after buds have formed but before they open. This will encourage plants to bush out and produce more leaves, right up to the first frost.

PREPARATION

Use fresh leaves. Boiling intensifies the peppery flavor and spicy scent.

Fresh Basil Ale *

1 gallon water	1 t yeast
1 C brown sugar	1 gallon glass jar (fermenter)
1 1/2 C unhopped amber malt extract	1 plastic bag
15-18 fresh Basil tops, about 3-4 inches each	1 elastic band

Boil water, sugar, and malt extract, covered, for 30 minutes. Add Basil, boil 15 minutes more. This boil yields the "wort," the sweetened herbal decoction which is the basis of every ale. Remove wort from heat, strain, cover, and let cool to room temperature, 6-7 hours. Make a disinfectant herbal infusion and rinse all brewing equipment (see p. 25). Pour the cooled wort into the clean fermenter. Add 1 t brewer's yeast dissolved in 1/2 C water. Cover the fermenter's opening with the plastic bag, and secure with the elastic band. Label, date, and leave undisturbed to ferment for a week or until bubbles subside. Bottle and store in a cool place for at least 2 weeks and up to 4 months. Improves with age.

* More about home brewing, basic ingredients and equipment, and step-by-step directions on page 22.

Borage *Borago officinalis, Bee Bread*

Borage for courage! The old folk saying still holds true, since Borage is a tonic herb that strengthens the nerves. Brewing Borage makes available more of its essential fatty acids, which help to balance hormones and nourish the nervous system. Midwives recommend Borage ale to increase a nursing mother's milk supply, and to prevent post-partum depression.

USES

○ Provides tonic nourishment
○ Supplies essential fatty acids
○ Strengthens the nervous system
○ Balances hormones
○ Relieves depression & lifts spirits

CULTIVATION

Sow directly outside in early spring or fall, in a sunny, well-drained spot. Cover seeds completely as they need darkness to germinate. Borage is an annual, but once established it will usually self sow. This excellent bee plant grows up to 3 feet high, with rough, hairy leaves and brilliant blue star-shaped flowers with distinctive black centers. Harvest the leaves and flowers when the plant is in full bloom. To prepare leaves for drying, fold lengthwise and tear out the thick watery spine of each leaf. Place flowers and torn leaves on screens or newspapers to dry in a cool place out of direct sunlight.

PREPARATION

Use fresh or dried flowers and leaves. You can also steep Borage in wine for several days for another nutritious drink with a light spicy taste.

Borage Ale

1 gallon water	1 gallon glass jar
1 lb brown sugar	1 clear plastic bag
1 oz. dried Borage (or 2 oz. fresh)	1 elastic band
1 t yeast or 1/4 C yeast starter *	1 unbleached muslin tea bag

Put the Borage into the tea bag. Boil water, sugar, and Borage for 30 minutes. Cool to 70°. Remove the Borage, and pour the wort into the clean fermenter. Add dissolved yeast or yeast starter. Ferment up to 2 weeks, or until bubbles subside. Bottle and store in a cool place for 10 days before drinking.

This is a basic ale recipe that you can use with any of the herbs in Alewife's Garden, and many other herbs, as well. Try brewing your own favorites this way.

* More about yeast starters on page 22.

Caraway *Carum carvi, Caraway Seed*

Caraway has been used for over 5,000 years as a food, flavoring, and digestive aid. Fermented, it makes a delicious, rich, and flavorful brew which is also useful in cooking. All Caraway preparations settle the stomach and support digestion.

USES

- ○ Provides tonic nourishment
- ○ Aids digestion
- ○ Relieves gas pains
- ○ Flavors vegetables, grains, fish, & meats

CULTIVATION

Sow Caraway outside in fall for a seed crop the following summer. It does best in full sun, and requires regular watering. Caraway grows up to 2 feet high on hollow, grooved stems, and produces tiny white flowers in small clusters. The double-pointed seeds are grooved, too. Harvest when the seeds turn brown. To dry completely, hang stems upside down in small bunches tied in brown paper bags to catch the seeds. Leave some seeds on the plant to self sow.

PREPARATION

Use the dried seeds. This ale also makes a piquant baste for baked winter vegetables, and an excellent marinade.

Caraway Ale

1 gallon water	1 gallon glass jar
1 lb. unhopped lager malt	1 plastic bag
1/2 lb. brown sugar	1 elastic band
1/4 oz. Caraway seeds	1 unbleached muslin tea bag
1 t yeast	

Put the Caraway seeds into the muslin bag. Boil the malt, sugar, water, and Caraway seeds together, covered, for 30 minutes. Remove the wort from the heat and steep until it reaches 70°. Remove the seeds and pour the wort into the clean fermenter. Dissolve the yeast in 1/2 cup of water and add it to the wort. Cover the mouth of the fermenter with the plastic bag, and secure with the elastic band. Label, date, and leave to ferment for about a week or until the bubbles subside. Bottle, cap, and store in a cool place for at least 10 days.

Roasted Winter Vegetables

Fill a roasting pan with diced fresh beets, butternut squash, sweet potatoes, pearl onions, and garlic. Add a handful each of shelled pistachio nuts and dried cranberries. Moisten with a cup or more of Caraway Ale, salt and pepper to taste, and drizzle with olive oil. Roast at 350° for 45 minutes or until tender.

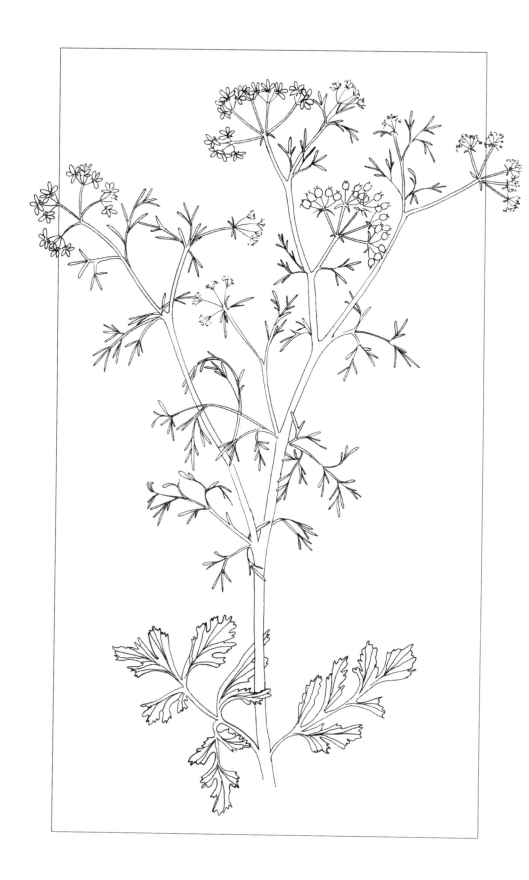

Coriander _Coriandrum sativum, Cilantro_

Coriander was believed by the ancient Chinese to promote immortality, and its seeds were burned as offerings in Egyptian tombs. Medicinally, Coriander is a bold and bitter digestive and appetite stimulant, so the ale makes an excellent aperitif. Coriander also calms upset stomachs, relieves gas pains and cramps, and supports the process of heavy metal detoxification. The spicy citrus flavor and aroma of the seeds reputedly stimulate the appetite for passion.

USES
- Provides tonic nourishment
- Stimulates appetite & supports digestion
- Treats mercury poisoning
- Excites passion

CULTIVATION

Annual Coriander is slow to germinate but easy to grow. Soak seeds overnight and sow outside in early spring, in well-drained, slightly alkaline soil and full sun. Be sure to cover seeds completely. Thin to 8 inches between seedlings, and don't fertilize as this will reduce the final flavor. Coriander's feathery light green leaves look similar to Italian Parsley until it shoots up to 3 feet high and blooms with bunches of tiny white flower heads. Once the seeds ripen, the plant's sharp aroma changes to a lovely citrus scent. Let the seeds dry on the stem, and harvest when they turn brown. If you leave some seeds behind, Coriander will self sow into late fall.

PREPARATION

Use the seeds, dried. Add dried roots to the wort for a nutty flavor. Alcohol extracts the beneficial qualities of Coriander seeds more effectively than water, so you may want to add one-half of the seeds directly to the fermenter as in this recipe. This is called "dry hopping."

Dry Hopped Coriander Honey Ale *

1 gallon water	2 clementine (or other citrus) peels
1 lb. brown sugar	1/2 C raw honey with royal jelly
1/2 oz. dried Coriander seeds	1" sliver of fresh Ginger root
1t yeast	1 unbleached muslin tea bag

Put half of the Coriander seeds in a muslin tea bag, and boil with the brown sugar and clementine peels for 30 minutes. Strain the wort, cool to 70 degrees, and stir in the honey. Pour into clean fermenter. Dissolve the yeast in 1/2 C of water and add it to the wort. Cover, label, and let the yeast work for at least two days. Put the remaining Coriander seeds and the sliver of Ginger root in a muslin tea bag, add to the wort, and leave it to finish fermenting. (Honey ales will take up to three months longer to complete fermentation than other ales.) Clean, fill, and cap bottles, and age 10 days before drinking.

* More about dry hopping and honey fermentations on page 23.

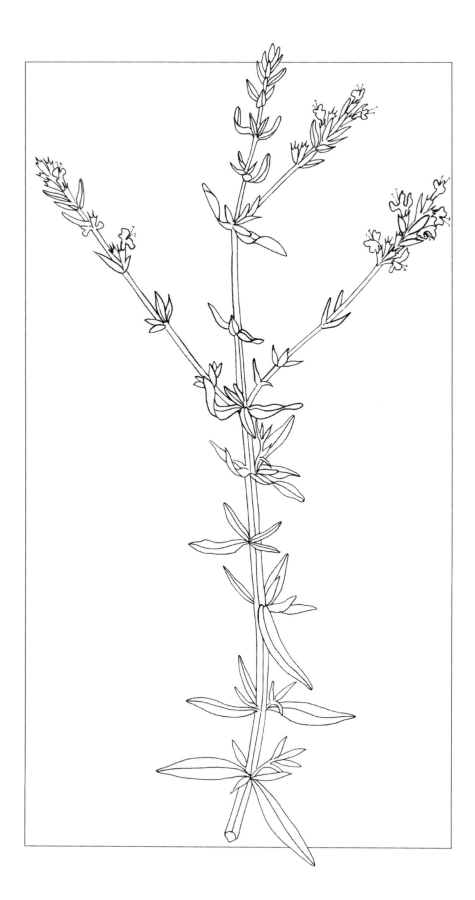

Hyssop *Hyssopus officinalis, Sermon Mint*

Hyssop's beneficial properties and pungent taste have long made it a favorite brewing herb, and it is also used to flavor the liqueurs Benedictine and Chartreuse. Hyssop is mildly sedative, and its bitter taste improves digestion. It is decongestive and strongly anti-viral, making it useful for treating coughs, colds, and flu. Use a Hyssop infusion to disinfect brewing equipment.

USES
○ Provides tonic nourishment
○ Decongests mucus
○ Supports digestion
○ Relaxes the nervous system
○ Disinfects brewing equipment

CULTIVATION
Start Hyssop inside or out in early spring. It prefers sun, and will flourish in dry rocky spots. This shrubby perennial evergreen can grow to 1.5 feet on branching, square stems typical of the Mint family. It may bloom in the first year, producing little blue flowers on spikes in early summer. Harvest the leaves just before the flowers open. Bees, butterflies, and hummingbirds love Hyssop, so do leave some blooms for them. Hang stems upside down to dry in a cool place out of direct light.

PREPARATION
Use fresh or dried leaves. Dry hopping intensifies the minty aroma and taste.

Stephen Buhner's Hyssop Ale
1 gallon water
1 1/2 C unsulphured organic molasses
1 C brown sugar
1/2 oz. dried Hyssop
1t yeast

1 gallon glass jar
1 clear plastic bag
1 elastic band
1 unbleached muslin tea bag

Put the Hyssop in the tea bag. Boil molasses, sugar, water, and Hyssop for 30 minutes. Cool the wort to 70°, strain, and pour into clean fermenter. Leave undisturbed to finish fermenting, approximately 1 week. Funnel into bottles and cap. Ready to drink in 2 weeks.

Hyssop Infusion
Put a handful of Hyssop into a quart glass jar and pour in boiling water to cover. Cap and steep while the wort cools, 6-7 hours. Strain, and use the infusion to rinse the clean fermenter, plastic bag, and elastic band before pouring in the wort. When the brew has fully fermented in a week or so, make another Hyssop infusion to disinfect your bottles before filling them. (You can also use Yarrow in this way.) This infusion will disinfect your brewing equipment without toxicity.

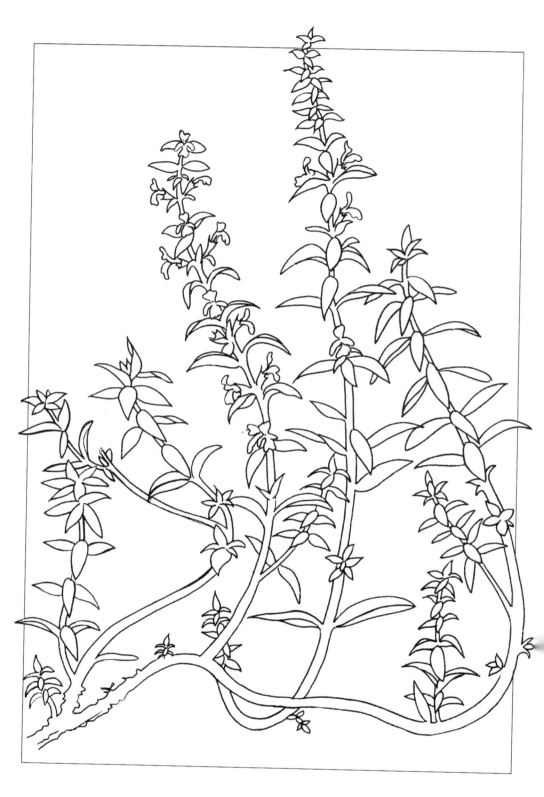

Winter Savory

Satureja montana,
Mountain Savory

Like other Mints, tonic Winter Savory stimulates the appetite and relieves stomach upset, diarrhea, and gas. It makes a particularly useful digestive aid when taken with foods that are difficult to digest. It is mildly antiseptic and drying, as well as soothing for sore throat and cough. Although its contemporary use is primarily culinary and medicinal, the ancient Egyptians frequently used Winter Savory in love potions.

Uses
○ Provides tonic nourishment
○ Stimulates appetite & supports digestion
○ Soothes stomach upsets & gas pains
○ Relieves diarrhea
○ Excites passion

Cultivation
Start Winter Savory inside in early spring. Don't cover the seeds, as they need light to germinate. Transplant outside to a place in full sun, with good drainage. Sandy soil or even a rocky spot will work, or you can grow it in a container. Perennial Winter Savory will grow up to 18 inches high, with tough narrow leaves and tiny pinkish flowers on straight stems. The whole plant is very aromatic. Harvest leaves when flowers are in bud. Pinching back will encourage new growth and a bushy shape.

Preparation
Use the leaves, fresh or dried. Winter Savory Ale makes a delicious peppery marinade. Use it in place of wine in coq au vin for a fabulous gourmet treat.

Winter Savory Ale

1 gallon water	1 gallon glass jar
1 1/2 C unhopped malt extract	1 clear plastic bag
1 C brown sugar	1 elastic band
2 oz. Winter Savory, fresh or dried	1 unbleached muslin tea bag
1t yeast	

Boil the malt extract, sugar, and water for 30 minutes. Add 1 oz. Winter Savory in a muslin tea bag and boil 10 more minutes. Strain and cover the wort, let cool to 70°, and pour into clean fermenter. Dissolve the yeast in 1/2 C water and add to the wort. Cover and leave until fully fermented, about a week. Bottle and store in a cool place. Ready to drink in 2 weeks. It improves with age. For a spicier brew, try dry hopping. Let the wort ferment for a couple of days, then add another ounce of Winter Savory in a teabag. Finish fermenting, remove the herb, and funnel into clean bottles.

Yarrow *Achillea millefolium, Sanguinary*

Yarrow is an ancient favorite brewing herb, both on its own and as a flavorful and potentiating additive to other brews. Valued worldwide for its bitter flavor, it also has notably inebriating and aphrodisiac effects when fermented. An antiseptic and astringent Yarrow infusion serves well as a general disinfectant for brewing equipment. Indeed, its antibiotic properties are so strong that Yarrow fermentations often take longer because the herb inhibits the yeast's power. Yarrow contains thujone, considered a "narcotic poison" by the FDA. We enjoy Yarrow Ale very much.

USES

○ Provides tonic nourishment
○ Stimulates appetite & supports digestion
○ Excites passion
○ Flavors and strengthens other brews
○ Disinfects brewing equipment

CULTIVATION

Perennial Yarrow grows anywhere, but prefers sun and acid soil. It easily spreads on its own once it is established. Sow in spring, indoors or out, but don't cover the tiny seeds as they need light to germinate. Yarrow's dark green, fernlike leaves grow on straight stalks up to 3 feet high, with wide flat heads of small white flowers that bloom from late spring right up to frost. Harvest the top third of the plant in full bloom. To dry, hang upside down in small bunches out of direct light.

PREPARATION

Use the fresh flowerheads. The larger the flower and the darker the leaf, the stronger the ale.

Yarrow Ale

1 gallon water	1 gallon glass jar
1 lb. brown sugar	1 plastic bag
1 1/2 oz. fresh Yarrow	1 elastic band
1 t yeast	2 unbleached muslin tea bags

Boil the water with the sugar for 30 minutes. Divide the Yarrow between the tea bags, add one to the pot, and boil another 5 minutes. Cover and let cool to 70°. Remove the tea bag and pour the wort into the fermenter. Add the dissolved yeast and the second tea bag of Yarrow, and cover the opening with the plastic bag, secured with the elastic. Label, date, and leave to finish fermenting. (Remember this will take longer than other brews.) Funnel into bottles and store in a cool, dark place. Ready to drink in 2 weeks. Dry hopping with fresh Yarrow strengthens any brew.

Starting Seeds Indoors & Out

Your postcard for seven free seed packets is on page 27. You'll find all the specific instructions needed to cultivate your seeds on the back of each seed packet. Also, be sure to refer to the cultivation information on the page for each plant in this book. For more about propagating seeds and cultivating weeds, check the list of Additional Resources on page 26.

STARTING SEEDS INDOORS

Start with a sterile potting mix of about 80% peat (to hold moisture) and 20% perlite (for drainage). Add a little water to the mix and stir it up with your hands until it's soft and fluffy. Scoop the mix into a seedling tray (or a paper cup or an egg carton — you can use anything you can poke a hole in for bottom drainage), scrape off the excess, and tamp down. Shake the seed out carefully. Don't sow too thickly, as it will stunt seedling growth and make it difficult to separate and transplant later on. The rule of thumb is to plant seeds about twice as deep as they are long.

Make a label for each different variety of seed. (You can buy markers at a nursery, or recycle popsicle sticks.) Cover the seeds with a layer of vermiculite for water retention and protection. Place on a tray in a warm spot with bright but not direct light, and wet thoroughly with warm water, preferably using a mister. Keep the growing mixture moist until the seeds sprout. To avoid rot, water only in the morning. If your house is dry, place a humidity dome (or a plastic bag with a few holes poked in it) over the seed tray. Take it off as soon as seedlings appear, or they'll get too leggy.

Seedlings usually appear in 7-21 days, but sometimes take longer, depending on the variety. Whenever they come up, they'll continue to need lots of light but not so much heat or water. For strong stem development, it's best to keep them on the dryish side. Water from the bottom as needed. When the first real leaves appear, begin to feed weekly with a half-strength solution of water-soluble, organic fertilizer that will provide an even ratio (20-20-20) of nitrogen for growth, phosphorus for flowers and roots, and potash for strong stems.

When the seedlings have two sets of real leaves, you can transplant them: first to small pots and then, when they're about 6 inches high, outside. Before transplanting seedlings to your garden, harden them off for a week or so by putting them outside during the day and bringing them inside to an unheated garage or porch at night.

Starting seeds outdoors

This method is called "direct seeding." Wait until all danger of frost is past. Rake thoroughly to break up the soil surface. Mix seeds with a little sand for a more even broadcast when you sow. Scatter seeds in the loose dirt, then rake again to cover lightly. Keep the area uniformly moist until seeds sprout. Water regularly for about six weeks or until seedlings are well established. Thereafter, water and feed as necessary.

Special seed treatments
SOAKING

Whether you sow your seeds indoors or out, pre-treating any hard-coated seeds will help them to germinate. Soaking is the easiest treatment method. Cover seeds with warm water and soak for 24 hours. Most of them will expand several sizes during this period. (Those that don't may not germinate, but try planting them, anyway.) Sow immediately; don't let the seeds dry out.

Germination and maturation

Hyssop, Winter Savory, and Yarrow are perennials. Once they are established in your garden, they will come back for many years with very little effort on your part. Caraway is generally considered a biennial, best sown in fall for seeds the following season.

Basil, Borage, and Coriander are annuals which will mature quickly and may self-sow, especially in warmer areas. With care and good growing conditions, you will be able to use almost all of these plants within a few months of sowing the seeds.

This chart outlines the preferred sowing method and approximate times to germination and harvest for each of the seven radical weeds in alewife's Garden. While your garden grows, you can make many of the ales in this book using dried organic herbs.

Plant	Preferred Sowing Method	Approximate Time to Germination	Approximate Time to Useful Stage of Growth
Basil	direct seed in spring	7-10 days	1-2 months to leaves
Borage	direct seed in early spring	7-10 days	1-2 months to leaves & flowers
Caraway	direct seed in fall	10-14 days	10 months to seeds
Coriander	soak & direct seed in early spring	2 weeks	1-2 months to seeds
Hyssop	direct seed in early spring	7-10 days	2-3 months to leaves
Winter Savory	sow indoors in spring, don't cover	2 weeks	2-3 months to leaves
Yarrow	direct seed in spring, don't cover	10-14 days	2-3 months to leaves & flowers

Harvesting & Storing Plants & Seeds

FLOWERS & LEAVES

The best time to harvest is in the morning on a sunny day, as soon as all the dew is dry. This is when the plant's essential oils will be at their peak strength. Whenever you pick, always leave some plants behind to go to seed. If you're harvesting plant material to dry, or to use in an oil infusion, be sure to pick when the plants are dry to begin with. If you're harvesting to make a tincture or water infusion right away, you can pick in the rain, but you won't get the full strength of the plant.

If you don't plan to use your harvest right away, tie bunches of stems together and hang upside down, or spread on screens or newspaper, in a dry, cool, dark room. Drying time depends on the weather and the plant part. It can take two days to two weeks. Plants are dry when the thickest part snaps or crunches to touch. Store in brown paper bags, labelled with name and date, in a cool, dry place. Under these storage conditions, potency lasts at least a year.

It's not necessary to strip leaves and flowers from stems before storage. In fact, breaking the plant down this way will increase oxidation, which will release the plant's stored energy much more quickly. To maintain freshness and potency, store your dried herbs whole, and crush or powder them only when you are ready to use them.

ROOTS

The usual time to harvest roots is in the fall, after the plant has flowered and gone to seed. You can also harvest roots in early spring, before they send up stalks. Dig roots out carefully, and sever with a sharp trowel, knife, or hand-ax. Use a toothbrush to remove all dirt, chop into small pieces, and use fresh if indicated. Dry chopped roots on a screen or newspaper out of direct light in a cool, dry place. Store in brown paper bags, labelled and dated. Dried roots retain potency for years.

SEEDS

Most herb seeds are easily gathered by hand after flower petals have fallen away and stems have begun to dry. Alternatively, you can cut bunches of dried stems and hang them upside down in paper bags. The seeds will eventually fall into the bags and you can retrieve them for storage. Whichever gathering method you use, most of your seeds should remain viable for a couple of years if you store them in a dry, cool place. Many garden supply stores sell blank seed packets, or you can use your own envelopes. Label, date, and store.

Brewing Simple Ales

"Brewing is a messy, chaotic, wet, stimulating, and strenuous activity that produces euphoria and health — sort of like sex." **Sacred and Herbal Healing Beers**

We'll drink to that! And you can, too. Here's an annotated list of the 4 basic ingredients and the simple equipment you'll need to make one gallon of herbal ale, followed by a step-by-step description of the brewing process, from boiling the water to filling — and opening — the bottles. Cheers!

Ingredients

YEAST

Yeasts are one-celled fungi that float freely throughout our world, living everywhere, tolerating almost all conditions, and knowing no boundaries. They can use any source of sugar for nourishment, lying dormant for long periods until they find one. As they consume sugar, they naturally produce alcohol and carbon dioxide as metabolic byproducts. Adding yeast to the wort (the boiled water, sugar, and herb) begins the fermentation. An active fermentation is said to be "boiling" as the froth builds, and the working yeast is in a "smiling" condition.

For ease in brewing, we make our invocations using packaged yeast. You can get ale yeast at any brewer's supply store (see Additional Resources, page 26). We've had good luck with SafAle, and with Danstar brand yeasts like Manchester, Windsor, Nottingham, and London. Each of them will make a different tasting ale.

Whatever your choice, do use yeast cultured for brewing, not baking yeast or the nutritional brewer's yeast sold in health food stores. The brewing process itself will create yeast starters for ales just like sourdough starter does for bread. Save those from your best ales to make another batch.

SUGAR

Almost any source of sugar can be used with the notable exception of plain, white, table sugar, which ruins ale. Any combination of light or dark brown sugar and molasses is tasty, and these sweeteners can also be used alone. Canned barley malt, available at brewing supply stores, adds a nutty flavor and increases the clarity of the brew. Use malt extracts alone for a lighter, drier ale. We like Mt. Mellick Irish Unhopped Amber Malt extract and Morgan's Master Lager Malt Blend.

Of course, no alewife's kitchen would be complete without raw honey, which was used for perhaps the oldest fermented potables. Honey, prized as a tonic for glowing health, long life, and soul inspiration, works well as an additive to any fermentation, and also on its own. A fermentation using honey as its only source of sugar is called mead. Since the carbohydrates of the honey take longer for the yeast to break down than those in other sugars like molasses or malt, meads take up to three months longer to ferment, and at least a year to age to perfection.

Home brewers often add a pinch of sugar to bottles before filling to boost carbonation through yeast action after bottling. This is known as "priming" the bottles. However, adding just a bit too much sugar can lead to an exploding bottle, resulting in a serious injury. For safety's sake if you do decide to prime your bottles, we recommend using the crimp style bottle caps. They should give way under pressure before the bottle does.

Through years of experimentation, we have found that priming is unnecessary, so we never do it anymore. Herbal ales have a unique flavor and character and also unique levels of natural carbonation. Some are more like wines. Some, including honey fermentations, begin to bubble in the glass only as they warm to room temperature. Others, like Caraway and Borage, are more boldly fizzy right out of the bottle.

HERB

In most cases, fresh is better, and Basil must be used fresh. Use Caraway and Coriander seeds dry. With any of the other herbs, you can use a combination of fresh and dry.

Of course, the seven herbs in Alewife's Garden aren't the only ones that make delicious ales. We've had excellent results brewing Rosemary, Hawthorn berry, Calendula, and Bee Balm, among others. We recommend using the basic ale recipe on page 7 to experiment with any of these herbs, and with your own favorites as well. At worst, you'll feed your compost pile!

Adding herbs to the fermenting wort while it's in a smiling condition is called "dry hopping." Dry hopping creates a stronger tasting ale and a doubly powerful remedy, as the alcohol produced by the yeast extracts the added plant's essence — in effect, tincturing it. You can dry hop with the principal brewing herb or use a different herb, for flavor and/or strength.

A few words here about the herb Hops. Hops is a perennial climbing vine with fragrant flowers and bitter, soporific, and antiseptic properties. Technically, a brew made with Hops flowers is called beer, not ale. We use no Hops in these recipes but rather traditional brewing herbs in common use long before Hops. Adding Hops to any of the recipes in Alewife's Garden will produce a brew that tastes more like modern beers. It will also make you sleepy! If you like the taste of Hops, use a hopped malt extract for your sweetener, or add Hops to the fermenter while the yeast is in a smiling condition. For the strongest Hops beer, use Hops alone. An infusion of Hops also makes an effective disinfectant for brewing equipment.

WATER

Use pure water. If you don't drink your tap water, then don't use it to make ale. Use bottled or distilled water if you don't have a clean water source.

Equipment

FERMENTER

one-gallon glass jar (wide mouth)

clear plastic bag

elastic band

Once you transfer the wort into the clean jar, cover the jar mouth loosely with the clean plastic bag, and secure it in place with the elastic band. As the fermentation progresses, it will produce enough carbon dioxide to inflate the plastic bag.

MUSLIN TEA BAGS

Use unbleached cotton bags to contain the herbs in the wort, and for dry hopping. Otherwise, you'll have to strain out loose herbs while transferring the wort into or out of the fermenter.

FUNNEL

Use to pour the ale from the fermenter into the bottles.

BOTTLES

Any recycled beer bottles will do, but Grolsch beer bottles are easiest because they have a reusable flip top with a rubber gasket. Otherwise, you'll need to purchase a supply of bottle caps, and a crimper to put them on securely.

Optional Equipment

THERMOMETER

Use to check the temperature of the cooling wort. An instant meat thermometer works fine.

HYDROMETER

Use to determine when the yeast has finished consuming all sugar. This is good to know because if you bottle wort that has not finished fermenting, it could explode the bottle when the pressure gets too high. If you don't use a hydrometer, wait until the wort stops boiling and the froth subsides completely before bottling.

Process

You can do steps 1-6 in one day. The rest of the process will take 3-4 weeks to complete, including fermentation and aging in the bottles.

> Steps 1-3 take about 8 hours, most of it boiling and cooling time
> Steps 4-6 take 20-30 minutes
> Step 7 takes a week or two
> Steps 8-9 take 20-30 minutes
> Step 10 takes 10 days to 2 weeks

1. Bring the water and sugar to a boil in a stainless steel pot and simmer-boil for at least 30 minutes, covered. Put the herb in a muslin tea bag and add it to the boil. Some recipes call for adding the herb for the whole cooking time, some only at the end. The sweetened herbal decoction is called the "wort".

2. Remove the wort from the heat and let cool to room temperature (70° F), covered. This will take about 6-7 hours. The strength of the brew will depend on how long you leave the herb infusing in the wort. Remove the herb before transferring the wort to the fermenter.

3. While the wort cools, make an infusion of an antiseptic herb to disinfect the fermenter. Suitable herbs include Hyssop, Yarrow, Sage, Hops, and Rosemary. Place a large handful of dried herb into a quart jar and cover with boiling water. Cap and steep about 6-7 hours. Strain before using.

4. Wash and rinse the fermenter, plastic bag, and elastic. Rinse the equipment again using the disinfectant herbal infusion.

5. Dissolve 1 teaspoon of yeast in half a cup of water.

6. Pour the cooled wort into the clean fermenter, add the dissolved yeast, and cover the mouth of the jar loosely with the clean plastic bag, securing the bag in place with the elastic band. The yeast may take a day to begin smiling. Eventually, carbon dioxide will inflate the plastic bag.

7. Label and date, and leave undisturbed at room temperature until the yeast has consumed the sugar. The signs that fermentation has finished are absence of foam on the surface and no more visible bubbling. This usually takes 1-2 weeks. Before you bottle, make another disinfectant infusion and steep it overnight.

8. Wash and rinse funnel, glass bottles, and caps. Rinse everything again using the disinfectant herbal infusion.

9. Pour the wort through the clean funnel into the prepared bottles, leaving the bottle neck empty for head room. Pour the yeasty residue from the bottom of the fermenter into a glass jar, label, and refrigerate. Use 1/4 C of yeast starter to brew your next batch of ale.

10. Cap, label, date, and store bottles in a cool place like a cellar or porch to age until ready, usually 10 days to 2 weeks. Many herbal ales improve with age, if you can wait to drink them! Always take care opening bottles. Wrap in a dish cloth and aim away from your face.

Additional Resources

Recommended books about brewing radical weeds:

SACRED AND HERBAL HEALING BEERS
by Stephen Harrod Buhner
Siris Books, 1998

THE HOMEBREWER'S GARDEN
by Joe Fisher & Dennis Fisher
Storey Books, 1998

THE HISTORICAL COMPANION TO HOUSE-BREWING
by Clive LaPensée
Montag Publications, 1990

MAKING MEAD
by Bryan Acton & Peter Duncan
Argus Books, Ltd., 1984

Recommended books about propagation and cultivation:

RODALE'S ILLUSTRATED ENCYCLOPEDIA OF HERBS
Claire Kowalchik & William H. Hylton, eds.
Rodale Press, 1987

PARK'S SUCCESS WITH SEEDS
by Ann Reilly
Geo. W. Park Seed Co., Inc., 1978

PARK'S SUCCESS WITH HERBS
by Gertrude B. Foster and Rosemary F. Louden
Geo. W. Park Seed Co., Inc., 1980

Recommended suppliers:

RADICAL REMEDIES
321 Anawan Street
Rehoboth, MA 02769
remedies@radicalweeds.com

One-stop source for dried organic herbs for brewing. Owned and operated by coauthor Jillian VanNostrand. Free brochure.

For yeasts, malts, bottles, caps, crimpers, books, and optional equipment, try your local brewing supplies store. If there's none near you, enter "brewing supplies" in any search engine on the web to locate a mail order source.